UNEARTHING YOU

UNEARTHING YOU

Discover the Rituals, Values, and Practices that Make You, You

Rituals and Images by Marlon Hall

Sweet Sangoma Publishing Co. books may be purchased for educational, business, or sales promotional use. For more information, please email info@ sweetsangoma.com

Sweet Sangoma Publishing Co. website: www.sweetsangoma.com

FIRST SWEET SANGOMA PAPERBACK EDITION PUBLISHED IN 2018.

Designed by Marlon Hall

ISBN-13: 978-0-692-14518-0

Dear Phoenix,

When you sing,
I cry a smile.

When we laugh,
I laugh a cry.

This book is dedicated to you and how
you rise from the ashes of burned
expectations and exceed them with just
one smile.

I love you.

UNEARTHING YOU

FORWARD

A Supreme Dreamer

It was the best smoothie known to man, Green
Chocolate at Eat Gallery in Houston, Texas.
That's the first time I met Marlon Hall, my
fellow dreamer. I had no idea he was a
minister until I attended a wedding that he
administered. I stopped by the Eat Gallery
afterward, and he was behind the counter. I
said to him "I had no idea you were a
minister", he said to me "this is my
ministry now". With that he unearthed and
ushered a dynamic group of chef's into the
Houston community. That is Marlon Hall.
The person who makes dreamers become
believers.

Eventually, I began to attend worship
services at the Awakenings Movement, my
beloved church of creative misfits. Marlon
Hall has a way of connecting to the human
experience that more people need to hear.
Any minister who can present a mother's day
sermon based on the lyrics of rapper MC Lyte
is cool with me. I've learned to use my own

creativity as my activism. I watched him
brilliantly explain John Coltrane's love
letter to God while breaking down the
stanza's of A Love Supreme.

The creative mind is never at rest, and
Marlon Hall clearly does not get sleep. His
vision as a film maker is brilliant. His
eye as a photographer is extraordinary. His
communication as a teacher is unparalleled.
His love as a father is supreme. As is
common in his teachings, Unearthing You will
teach you to tell better stories about
yourself to yourself. It will unearth and
nurture a natural spirit you did not know
you had within. Embrace this journey.
Engage in the practice of seeing, the ritual
of listening and learn the values of
feelings that unearth you.

Ann Y. Johnson, MFA

UNEARTHING YOU

earthy brown portals
and dusty palms

sunburnt red clay
woven within ///

digging for me,
digging me.

in awe again.

YOU NEED YOU,

RIGHT NOW.

Who will you be with
more than you?

Who will you
tickle,
talk to,
and lovingly disagree with more?

Out of the matrix of your mama's womb
you entered earth's atmosphere with an
inherent mushiness and inalienable
passion for yourself. However, over
time, the grit and grime of everyday
life has buried and covered up the
"youest" expression of "you" with shame,
doubt, and indecision - - and I am here
to remind you that YOU NEED YOU. And you
need you, RIGHT NOW!

Never in your life have you needed you more. This moment in human history is rich with opportunities to grow as a human being more than ever, but the crap of our past has covered up the promises of our future.

Using my practice as an anthropologist and my passion for people, I have designed this spiritual archaeological journey for you to unearth the values, rituals, and practices to awaken you to the fullest expression of yourself.

My hope is this series of practices will ignite a personal curiosity in you that will lead you back to the home you are already in. You will become an anthropologist of your personal culture and context. Your "first-self" is calling to you by something that predates your name. This journey is your response. This gentle guide will invite you to do a spiritual, archaeological dig to unearth the values, rituals, and

practices that make you the best version
of you possible.

NO NUMBERS &

ALL OF THE FOOD

I discovered my love for anthropology early. My friends and I used to get dropped off at the mall. All of my friends had one mission, "get girls' numbers". They roamed while I could be found in the food court safely stalking the people around me. As a virtuous voyeur, I gave them regional accents, family histories, and lines of conversations. Looking at subtle cues and details, I imagined their lives from birth to the present pretzel they were eating over a talk with their table mate. At the end of the day, I had no numbers but my curiosity for human culture would be fed in those mall food courts.

Later, I chose anthropology as my course of study and love. Anthropology is the

study of human culture and their
development. Anthropologists use
"participant observation" as a tool to
participate in the culture they want to
learn from.

In this guide, we will work together to
develop the:

* **Practices of seeing** that
  engage core beliefs,

* **Rituals of listening** that
  invite self-reflection, and

* **Values of feeling** that
  become mantras for your
  life and work.

This isn't really a journal. This is a
reliquary, a container for the holy
relic that my words and yours will
become as you process possibility and
pain. The experiences I have designed
in this "lil" book will make a big impact

in you and about you. I wrote it because,
well, I love you.

HOW TO USE

THIS RELIQUARY.

Since childhood, I used my hands and ears to furnish new ways for people to live with themselves and learn from others. I am the son of an educator and an upholsterer, the choreography of learning and functionally creating.

These pages recreate space to make a reliquary or special place for the best "you" possible. Each day has the same ritual of observing what is catalyzed by a different picture and quote. You will develop a rhythm of being that will become a habit of your humanity well beyond the experience of this book.

This 21 day unearthing journey will poetically equip you to become a soul anthropologist; an observer of your essence in three stanzas to begin your

week with a tool to put in your toolkit
as an anthropologist of you:

- STANZA ONE: **Eyes of an anthropologist** //// Seeing as a daily PRACTICE of personal power.

- STANZA TWO: **Ears of an anthropologist** /// Listening as a daily RITUAL for peace.

- STANZA THREE: **Heart of an anthropologist** /// Feeling as a lifelong VALUE of hope.

To be an anthropologist is to be human and to engage your humanity with deep listening and lifelong learning. By the end of these next 21 days, you will have tools to observe yourself when you feel like a foreigner in your own body. It will be a way to return to your own humanity when you feel lost.

I invite you to dedicate 30 minutes to yourself each day to enjoy the unearthing you journey:

1. Find a quiet place to sit comfortably.
2. Silently count down from 10 to 1 in your head.
3. Read the mantra, quote, or blessing in each section three times.
4. Respond to the following questions:
   - What does it say? (In your own words, re-articulate the quote.)
   - What does it mean? (If it were a billboard, what would it say to humankind?)
   - How does it move me? (In other words, how will I activate what I have read in my life?)

LET'S GET TO DIGGING YOU/////

SEEING WITH EYES OF AN ANTHROPOLOGIST AS A SEVEN DAY PRACTICE!

Anthropology is derived from the Greek words anthropo, meaning "speaking of human" and logia, meaning "study." Cultural Anthropologists use participant observation as the best tool to do their work to learn about culture. They participate in the culture they want to learn from as an observer.

They eat what the indigenous culture eats,
learn the language and the inside jokes,
dance the dances,
while looking for all of the subtle nuances that make the people who they are.

Use the next seven days to be a participant observer of you. Look at your life as an observer and find personal power wash over you as you see the difference between the life you want to lead and how life may be leading you in the opposite direction.

Caution: Be open to seeing the same life you have with new eyes. How? Great question. Thanks for asking. DON'T OVER LOOK WHAT IS FOR WHAT ISN'T.

Many of the assessments we give our lives, good or bad, have more to do with what we don't see than the grace of what is to be seen and not acknowledged. Look for the love you DO see to assess whether or not you have love. What we don't see should never cloud the judgement of what we do see.

Marlon F. Hall (American, 1972 -   )

untitled

*At the intersection of Almeda and Wheeler, The East, West,
South, and North arteries of Houston cross at the heart of
Green Seed Vegan, 2018 A layer of wood grain impressed
inside a layer of wood grain.*

THE **MANTRA** | | |

A mantra is a word or sound repeated to aid concentration in meditation. Read the following sentence as your mantra.

[I WAS BORN TO MAKE AN INDELIBLE MARK ON HUMANITY THAT NO ONE CAN ERASE AND IF I DON'T MAKE THAT MARK IT WON'T BE MADE./////]

1. Find a quiet place to sit comfortably.
2. Silently count down from 10 to 1 in your head.
3. Read the mantra or quote three times.
4. Respond to the following questions:
   - What does it say? (In your own words, re-articulate the quote.)
   - What does it mean? (If it were a billboard, what would it say to humankind?)
   - Have I seen this to be true in my life today? How?
     - How does it move me? (In other words, how will I activate what I have read in my life?)

DRAW.

WRITE!

Marlon F. Hall (American, 1972 -   )

rooting

At the basin of the Chocolate Bayou in Houston, this tree stands
seemingly wound up by the very roots that nurture its growth.

THE MANTRA] | | |

A mantra is a word or sound repeated to aid concentration in meditation. Read the following sentence as your mantra.

[COMFORT IS THE ENEMY OF MY CREATIVITY./////]

1. Find a quiet place to sit comfortably.
2. Silently count down from 10 to 1 in your head.
3. Read the mantra or quote three times.
4. Respond to the following questions:
   - What does it say? (In your own words, re-articulate the quote.)
   - What does it mean? (If it were a billboard, what would it say to humankind?)
   - Have I seen this to be true in my life today? How?
   - How does it move me? (In other words, how will I activate what I have read in my life?)

DRAW.

WRITE!

Marlon F. Hall (American, 1972 -   )

emerald rust

A wooden border to a pier in Downtown Houston. The green
water contrasted with the rust make for an ancient future
reflection of the sky.

THE MANTRA] | | |

A mantra is a word or sound repeated to aid concentration in meditation. Read the following sentence as your mantra.

[IT IS RISKY FOR ME TO BE SAFE AND SAFER FOR ME TO BE RISKY./////]

1. Find a quiet place to sit comfortably.
2. Silently count down from 10 to 1 in your head.
3. Read the mantra or quote three times.
4. Respond to the following questions:
   - What does it say? (In your own words, re-articulate the quote.)
   - What does it mean? (If it were a billboard, what would it say to humankind?)
   - Have I seen this to be true in my life today? How?
   - How does it move me? (In other words, how will I activate what I have read in my life?)

DRAW.

WRITE!

Marlon F. Hall *(American*, 1972 -   *)*

old gaming

The wall opposite a vintage arcade store reverse engineers the story of the store's appeal. Old games have new patrons.

THE MANTRA] | | |

A mantra is a word or sound repeated to aid concentration in meditation. Read the following sentence as your mantra.

[WHAT HAPPENED TO ME, ISN'T HAPPENING RIGHT NOW./////]

1. Find a quiet place to sit comfortably.
2. Silently count down from 10 to 1 in your head.
3. Read the mantra or quote three times.
4. Respond to the following questions:
   - What does it say? (In your own words, re-articulate the quote.)
   - What does it mean? (If it were a billboard, what would it say to humankind?)
   - Have I seen this to be true in my life today? How?
   - How does it move me? (In other words, how will I activate what I have read in my life?)

DRAW.

WRITE!

Marlon F. Hall (American, 1972 -   )

standing tall

An old pillar from an old bridge in Downtown Houston remains despite its new replacements.

THE MANTRA | | |

A mantra is a word or sound repeated to aid concentration in meditation. Read the following sentence as your mantra.

[I BLESS MYSELF WITH
   MY OWN POWER./////]

1. Find a quiet place to sit comfortably.
2. Silently count down from 10 to 1 in your head.
3. Read the mantra or quote three times.
4. Respond to the following questions:
   - What does it say? (In your own words, re-articulate the quote.)
   - What does it mean? (If it were a billboard, what would it say to humankind?)
   - Have I seen this to be true in my life today? How?
   - How does it move me? (In other words, how will I activate what I have read in my life?)

DRAW.

_____

_____

_____

_____

_____

_____

_____

_____

_____

_____

_____

_____

_____

WRITE!

Marlon F. Hall (American, 1972 -   )

innergrown

New growth replaces an opening in an uninhabited parking lot
wall.

THE MANTRA | | |

A mantra is a word or sound repeated to aid concentration in meditation. Read the following sentence as your mantra.

[I TELL THE BEST STORIES TO MYSELF, ABOUT MYSELF.////]

1. Find a quiet place to sit comfortably.
2. Silently count down from 10 to 1 in your head.
3. Read the mantra or quote three times.
4. Respond to the following questions:
   - What does it say? (In your own words, re-articulate the quote.)
   - What does it mean? (If it were a billboard, what would it say to humankind?)
   - Have I seen this to be true in my life today? How?
   - How does it move me? (In other words, how will I activate what I have read in my life?)

DRAW.

_____

_____

_____

_____

_____

_____

_____

_____

_____

_____

_____

_____

_____

_____

WRITE!

Marlon F. Hall (American, 1972 -   )

in and out

A door from Marlon's grandmother's home in Homer, Louisiana
hangs in his home as a way to remember where he came from.

THE MANTRA | | |

A mantra is a word or sound repeated to aid concentration in meditation. Read the following sentence as your mantra.

[BLESSED AM I WHEN I AM AT HOME WITH MYSELF, FOR WHEREVER I GO, I AM AT HOME./////]

1. Find a quiet place to sit comfortably.
2. Silently count down from 10 to 1 in your head.
3. Read the mantra or quote three times.
4. Respond to the following questions:
   - What does it say? (In your own words, re-articulate the quote.)
   - What does it mean? (If it were a billboard, what would it say to humankind?)
   - Have I seen this to be true in my life today? How?
   - How does it move me? (In other words, how will I activate what I have read in my life?)

DRAW.

WRITE!

LISTENING WITH THE EARS OF AN ANTHROPOLOGIST AS A SEVEN DAY RITUAL

////////////////

We all have a personal culture that develops daily for the good or for the best. Anthropology is the science of people study that can be used to master the art of being you. I call it the science of significance because we learn how to signify our humanity with a directed way of listening.

IN THIS SECTION WE WILL USE CALL AND RESPONSE. CALL AND RESPONSE IS A THREAD WOVEN INTO THE FABRIC OF AFRICAN AMERICAN CULTURE AND COMMUNICATION. THE CADENCE OF A PREACHER WAXING LOVELY AND THE RECORD SCRATCHING OF A DJ'S MUSIC SET ARE EVIDENCE OF A RHYTHMN OF LIFE "CALL AND RESPONSE" PROVOKE. THE

HEARTBEAT OF A DRUM HAS BEEN AN ARTFUL WAY TO SPEAK FROM ONE VILLAGE TO THE NEXT. THE CALL AND RESPONSE OF THIS "LISTENING" SECTION IS A POWERFUL WAY TO CALL TO THE CONSCIOUS MIND A RESPONSE FROM THE SUB-CONSCIOUS SOUL.

Caution: Listen to what is happening in life. Lean away from listening FOR what you need to be right about what you already think. Anthropology returns you to the original ways of listening that can empower human possibility or imprison you with human pain and suffering. Whole listening allows us to listen TO life rather than listen FOR what we need to hear to be right.

Open your mind to all that is happening and how it can all serve your life of listening to live.

Marlon F. Hall (American, 1972 -   )

fiery and concrete

As the sunsets the color of the golden time of day paints
concrete fire red and orange.

THE CALL' AND RESPONSE||||

THE CALL AND RESPONSE OF THIS "LISTENING" SECTION IS A POWERFUL WAY TO CALL TO THE CONSCIOUS MIND A RESPONSE FROM THE SUB-CONSCIOUS SOUL.

A SOULFUL ECHO OF THE INNER YOU!

[CALL: I INCITE A RIOT OF THE HEART THAT BURNS FOR BEAUTY.

RESPONSE: WITH PASSION I LOOT FOR LOVE. //////]

1. Find a quiet place to sit comfortably.
2. Silently count down from 10 to 1 in your head.
3. Read the CALL AND RESPONSE in each section three times.
4. Respond to the following questions:
   - What does it say? (In your own words, re-articulate the quote.)
   - What does it mean? (If it were a billboard, what would it say to humankind?)
   - Have I seen this to be true in my life today? How?

- How does it move me? (In other
  words, how will I activate what I
  have read in my life?)

DRAW.

WRITE!

Marlon F. Hall (American, 1972 -   )

switch

A gold painted light switch in Marlon's home was the first thing he engaged when walked into his space. It is a ritual of switching himself open to the sight of his own space

THE CALL AND RESPONSE||||

THE CALL AND RESPONSE OF THIS "LISTENING" SECTION IS A POWERFUL WAY TO CALL TO THE CONSCIOUS MIND A RESPONSE FROM THE SUB-CONSCIOUS SOUL.

A SOULFUL ECHO OF THE INNER YOU!

[CALL: IF MY POWER IS HIDDEN IN THE DARK.
RESPONSE: I SHINE A LIGHT ON IT AND I SHINE!/////]

1. Find a quiet place to sit comfortably.
2. Silently count down from 10 to 1 in your head.
3. Read the CALL AND RESPONSE three times.
4. Respond to the following questions:
   - What does it say? (In your own words, re-articulate the quote.)
   - What does it mean? (If it were a billboard, what would it say to humankind?)
   - Have I seen this to be true in my life today? How?
   - How does it move me? (In other words, how will I activate what I have read in my life?

DRAW.

WRITE!

Marlon F. Hall (American, 1972 -   )

doorway

*Door nestled under a bridge in downtown Houston where
Marlon and his daughter Phoenix scoot for adventure.*

THE CALL ' AND RESPONSE||||

THE CALL AND RESPONSE OF THIS "LISTENING" SECTION IS A POWERFUL WAY TO CALL TO THE CONSCIOUS MIND A RESPONSE FROM THE SUB-CONSCIOUS SOUL.

A SOULFUL ECHO OF THE INNER YOU!

[CALL: BECOME ALL YOU ARE,

RESPONSE: SURRENDER TO ALL THERE IS.//////]

1. Find a quiet place to sit comfortably.
2. Silently count down from 10 to 1 in your head.
3. Read the CALL AND RESPONSE three times.
4. Respond to the following questions:
   - What does it say? (In your own words, re-articulate the quote.)
   - What does it mean? (If it were a billboard, what would it say to humankind?)
   - Have I seen this to be true in my life today? How?
   - How does it move me? (In other words, how will I activate what I have read in my life?)

DRAW.

WRITE!

Marlon F. Hall (American, 1972 -   )

peak and boo

In Houston's warehouse district this artist's work comes to life in the ease of dusk.

THE CALL AND RESPONSE||||

THE CALL AND RESPONSE OF THIS "LISTENING" SECTION IS A POWERFUL WAY TO CALL TO THE CONSCIOUS MIND A RESPONSE FROM THE SUB-CONSCIOUS SOUL.

A SOULFUL ECHO OF THE INNER YOU!

[CALL: I AM NOT MY THOUGHTS.

RESPONSE: I AM NOT MY THOUGHTS.//////]

1. Find a quiet place to sit comfortably.
2. Silently count down from 10 to 1 in your head.
3. Read the CALL AND RESPONSE three times.
4. Respond to the following questions:
   - What does it say? (In your own words, re-articulate the quote.)
   - What does it mean? (If it were a billboard, what would it say to humankind?)
   - Have I seen this to be true in my life today? How?
   - How does it move me? (In other words, how will I activate what I have read in my life?)

DRAW.

WRITE!

Marlon F. Hall (American, 1972 -   )

walled war paint

Incidental art exists everywhere in Houston. This wall
incidentally reveals the feeling of war won and unmoved.

THE CALL' AND RESPONSE||||

THE CALL AND RESPONSE OF THIS
"LISTENING" SECTION IS A POWERFUL WAY
TO CALL TO THE CONSCIOUS MIND A
RESPONSE FROM THE SUB-CONSCIOUS SOUL.

A SOULFUL ECHO OF THE INNER YOU!

[CALL: MY PEACE IS NOT THE ABSENCE OF
PROBLEMS.

RESPONSE: MY PEACE IS THE PRESENCE OF
EASE AND A PLUNGE INTO HOPE.//////]

1. Find a quiet place to sit
   comfortably.
2. Silently count down from 10 to 1 in
   your head.
3. Read the CALL AND RESPONSE three
   times.
4. Respond to the following questions:
   - What does it say? (In your own
     words, re-articulate the quote.)
   - What does it mean? (If it were a
     billboard, what would it say to
     humankind?)
   - Have I seen this to be true in my
     life today? How?

- How does it move me? (In other words, how will I activate what I have read in my life?)

DRAW.

WRITE!

Marlon F. Hall (American, 1972 -   )

burnt and beautiful

An old and burned home left for demolition is the canvas for a beautiful sun set.

THE CALL AND RESPONSE||||

THE CALL AND RESPONSE OF THIS "LISTENING" SECTION IS A POWERFUL WAY TO CALL TO THE CONSCIOUS MIND A RESPONSE FROM THE SUB-CONSCIOUS SOUL.

A SOULFUL ECHO OF THE INNER YOU!

[CALL: I UNEARTH BEAUTY FROM MY BROKENNESS.

RESPONSE: I RISE FROM THE ASHES OF BURNT EXPECTATIONS.//////]

1. Find a quiet place to sit comfortably.
2. Silently count down from 10 to 1 in your head.
3. Read the CALL AND RESPONSE three times.
4. Respond to the following questions:
   - What does it say? (In your own words, re-articulate the quote.)
   - What does it mean? (If it were a billboard, what would it say to humankind?)
   - Have I seen this to be true in my life today? How?

- How does it move me? (In other
  words, how will I activate
  what I have read in my life?)

DRAW.

WRITE!

Marlon F. Hall (American, 1972 -   )

brick gardening

In an abandoned parking garage, life grows. Through the
cracks and on the crevices, life grows

THE CALL AND RESPONSE||||

THE CALL AND RESPONSE OF THIS "LISTENING" SECTION IS A POWERFUL WAY TO CALL TO THE CONSCIOUS MIND A RESPONSE FROM THE SUB-CONSCIOUS SOUL.

A SOULFUL ECHO OF THE INNER YOU!

[CALL: I GROW GREEN THROUGH THE CREVICES.

RESPONSE: I SEEK ROOTS IN THE CRACKS./////]

1. Find a quiet place to sit comfortably.
2. Silently count down from 10 to 1 in your head.
3. Read the CALL AND RESPONSE in each section three times.
4. Respond to the following questions:
   - What does it say? (In your own words, re-articulate the quote.)
   - What does it mean? (If it were a billboard, what would it say to humankind?)
   - Have I seen this to be true in my life today? How?

- How does it move me? (In other words, how will I activate what I have read in my life?

DRAW.

WRITE!

FEELING WITH THE HEART OF AN ANTHROPOLOGIST AS A SEVEN DAY RITUAL

///////////////

It is impossible to eliminate all personal and emotional biases, because we are human. We are story driven organisms. Some say the data an anthropologist discovers is tainted by emotional commitments. Our personal and emotional biases can sway what we see and hear as anthropologists. Might as well use what we cannot eliminate as a tool to illuminate the fullness of life where it can be observed.

In this section you will engage in the BLESSING. The blessing is like a toast to change and personal growth in the life of the person you are blessing. The

blessing is a canvas that we often use
to paint a portrait of new life and words
of truth and encouragement. Read the
blessing silently then state the
blessing aloud to yourself.

Caution: Feel from what you are FOR

and to from what you are AGAINST. When
we feel from what we are (FOR) we move
(for)ward. When we are emotionally led
by what we are against, we move
(AGAINST)ward, and where in the hell
does that guide us.

Marlon F. Hall (American, 1972 -   )

untitled

A picture of a picture taken by Marlon of his uncle, James Hall, who is a jet setting traveler who finds wholeness wherever he goes.

THE BLESSING||||

The blessing is like a toast to change and personal growth in the life of the person you are blessing.

[I AM HERE.

I AM NOW./////]

1. Find a quiet place to sit comfortably.
2. Silently count down from 10 to 1 in your head.
3. Read the BLESSING three times.
4. Respond to the following questions:
   - What does it say? (In your own words, re-articulate the quote.)
   - What does it mean? (If it were a billboard, what would it say to humankind?)
   - Have I seen this to be true in my life today? How?
   - How does it move me? (In other words, how will I activate what I have read in my life)

DRAW.

WRITE!

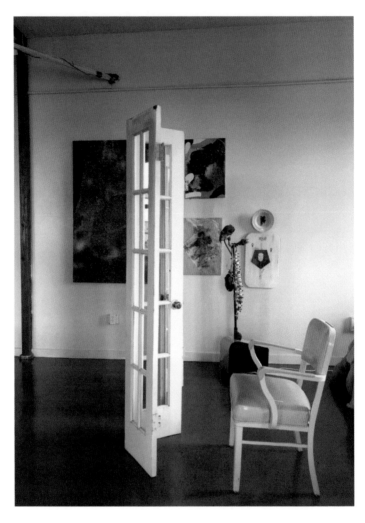

Marlon F. Hall (American, 1972 -   )

untitled

The French doors that led to Marlon's baby room when he was
an infant with the art work of Ann Johnson, Angelbert Metoyer,
Anthony Suber create safe place for being.

THE BLESSING||||

The blessing is like a toast to change
and personal growth in the life of the
person you are blessing.

[I AM DOING LESS

    TO BE MORE.//////]

1. Find a quiet place to sit
   comfortably.
2. Silently count down from 10 to 1 in
   your head.
3. Read the BLESSING three times.
4. Respond to the following questions:
   - What does it say? (In your own
     words, re-articulate the quote.)
   - What does it mean? (If it were a
     billboard, what would it say to
     humankind?)
   - Have I seen this to be true in my
     life today? How?
   - How does it move me? (In other
     words, how will I activate what I
     have read in my life)

DRAW.

WRITE!

Marlon F. Hall (American, 1972 -   )

untitled

Speakers framed in gold are an ode to the value music plays in vibrating the human spirit authentic.

THE BLESSING||||

The blessing is like a toast to change
and personal growth in the life of the
person you are blessing.

[I AM AUTHENTIC.

MY LACK OF AUTHENTICITY OVER A TIME
    FEELS LIKE A LACK OF HONESTY.//////]

1. Find a quiet place to sit
   comfortably.
2. Silently count down from 10 to 1 in
   your head.
3. Read the BLESSING three times.
4. Respond to the following questions:
   - What does it say? (In your own
     words, re-articulate the quote.)
   - What does it mean? (If it were a
     billboard, what would it say to
     humankind?)
   - Have I seen this to be true in my
     life today? How?
   - How does it move me? (In other
     words, how will I activate what I
     have read in my life)

DRAW.

WRITE!

Marlon F. Hall *(American, 1972 -   )*
untitled
In a moment of complexity, Marlon used these metal painted
letters he found as trash and turned them into an artful
expression he treasures in his home.

THE BLESSING||||

The blessing is like a toast to change and personal growth in the life of the person you are blessing.

[I TRASH NEGATIVE THOUGHTS,

IF I DON'T HAVE A TRASH CAN FOR MY CAR, MY CAR BECOMES ONE.//////]

1. Find a quiet place to sit comfortably.
2. Silently count down from 10 to 1 in your head.
3. Read the BLESSING three times.
4. Respond to the following questions:
   - What does it say? (In your own words, re-articulate the quote.)
   - What does it mean? (If it were a billboard, what would it say to humankind?)
   - Have I seen this to be true in my life today? How?
   - How does it move me? (In other words, how will I activate what I have read in my life)

DRAW.

WRITE!

Marlon F. Hall (American, 1972 -   )

untitled

This multi-toned wall under a bridge in downtown Houston is
cracked but still standing.

THE BLESSING||||

The blessing is like a toast to change
and personal growth in the life of the
person you are blessing.

[I AM INTENTIONAL.

MY LACK OF INTENTION OVER TIME

LOOKS LIKE A LACK OF INTEGRITY./////]

1. Find a quiet place to sit
   comfortably.
2. Silently count down from 10 to 1 in
   your head.
3. Read the BLESSING in each section
   three times.
4. Respond to the following questions:
   - What does it say? (In your own
     words, re-articulate the quote.)
   - What does it mean? (If it were a
     billboard, what would it say to
     humankind?)
   - Have I seen this to be true in my
     life today? How?
   - How does it move me? (In other
     words, how will I activate what I
     have read in my life)

DRAW.

WRITE!

Marlon F. Hall (American, 1972 -   )

untitled

The sun sets into the horizon with oranges, pinks, and blue
colors reflecting the light of day folding into night.

THE BLESSING||||

The blessing is like a toast to change
and personal growth in the life of the
person you are blessing.

[I HAVE THE POWER TO RAISE THE DEAD
INSIDE ME.//////]

1. Find a quiet place to sit
   comfortably.
2. Silently count down from 10 to 1 in
   your head.
3. Read the BLESSING in each section
   three times.
4. Respond to the following questions:
   - What does it say? (In your own
     words, re-articulate the quote.)
   - What does it mean? (If it were a
     billboard, what would it say to
     humankind?)
   - Have I seen this to be true in my
     life today? How?
   - How does it move me? (In other
     words, how will I activate what I
     have read in my life)

DRAW.

WRITE!

Marlon F. Hall (American, 1972 -   )

untitled

This scene in Cambutal, Panama features the sun rising out of the mountains where an ocean meets a jungle. Marlon stood on this rock formation each morning during the Yoga Teacher Training that resurrected his passion for life and love again.

THE BLESSING||||

The blessing is like a toast to change and personal growth in the life of the person you are blessing.

[MY CHOICE TO LIVE BREAKS THROUGH DEATH AND UNBINDS FREEDOM.//////]

1. Find a quiet place to sit comfortably.
2. Silently count down from 10 to 1 in your head.
3. Read the BLESSING in each section three times.
4. Respond to the following questions:
   - What does it say? (In your own words, re-articulate the quote.)
   - What does it mean? (If it were a billboard, what would it say to humankind?)
   - Have I seen this to be true in my life today? How?
   - How does it move me? (In other words, how will I activate what I have read in my life)

DRAW.

WRITE!

YOU ARE NOW AN ANTHROPOLOGIST OF YOU||||

You now have the tools to observe yourself when you feel like a foreigner in your own body. You have a way to return to your own humanity when you feel lost. You are an anthropologist of you. You are human. You now have tools to engage your humanity with deep listening and a skillset that will last you a lifetime.

You are
now an
Anthropologist of
you.

YOUR
PERSONAL
RELIQUARY

/// A FOUR WORD POEM RELIQUARY

A WAY TO REMEMBER YOU TO YOU.

////////

A reliquary is a safe space that holds sacred or family relics. Like the Arc of God's Covenant, Indiana Jones searched for the photo album grandma could reprimand you for playing with. This part of the book holds space for what you found out about yourself through the rituals so far.

This section of the journey is self-guided by your intuition and personal interest. It's a reliquary for whatever you want. Write with words, draw images, or scrapbook with found objects. This can serve as amnesia therapy at any time to recall you back to your calling in life.

THICK SMOKEY MIRROR

In 2017 I reimagined my relationship with my wife (got divorced), and it was traumatic. My daughter's pain, my disappointment, and our family's shame loomed in the loft I lived in. It was thick like smoke making it hard to see myself. I had lost my family and it was hard to remember who I was without them. I asked friends and fellow mess-makers Anthony //a sculptor// and Brian //a photographer// to help me turn some reclaimed wood from my grandmother's house, in Homer, Louisiana, into a long table for a traditional salon dinner party series to unearth beauty from brokenness.

I bring a cross-pollination of 16 people at a time to the table to remember the beauty of being human. It is a renegade anthropological study I am doing about human connection and purpose memory. Original musical composition, rich culinary art, and intentionally designed conversation drive a night of wonder; all shared by people who are different and share a heart for the city. In this room they cannot talk about what they do, only who they are and why they exist.

This part of the journey is made from the principles and values I learned at that table.

FOUR WORD POEM RITUAL

When I read a poem I don't have information, I have a new experience.
                              - E. Peterson

One of the rituals I do at my dinner parties to help people get away from

what they do and toward why they are is
poetry. I, specifically, invite guests
to practice the ritual of a four word
"Why" poem. It helps to unblock their
flow and communicate a deep knowing they
already have about themselves.

BABY SHOES AND WRITER'S BLOCK

Innovative writer, Ernest Hemingway was
experiencing writer's block. A friend
bet him that he couldn't write a
compelling story using just six words.

He responded to the challenge by
writing, *"For sale: baby shoes, never
worn."*

The friend paid up. Because this story
was uniquely rooted to Hemingway's
"why", he was relieved of his writer's
block and went on to use this exercise
when feeling stuck. This "why" moment in
an innovative man's life informed what

he would do as a writer for the rest of
his career.

Now, let's begin a similar ritual for
you.

HERE IS THE PROCESS

- **Location:** Find a quiet and
  comfortable place.

- **Silence:** Slowly breathe in and out
  three consecutive times. Quiet
  your thoughts by counting from 10
  to 0.

- **Reflect:** Think of a Verb, a Noun,
  a Preposition, and another Noun
  from. These four words will be
  your "FOUR WORD WHY POEM."

For example:

EXCAVATE (verb)

PURPOSE (noun)

FROM (preposition)

PAIN (noun)

Now allow yourself to think automatically (intuitively), then write the poem using the following format:

VERB,

NOUN,

PREPOSITION,

NOUN

Next, memorize your poem and write it at the top of each page in your reliquary.

Though the pages are now empty, they can be filled with impressions of your personal identity.

Remember, this section of the journey is self-guided by your intuition and personal interest. It's a reliquary for whatever you want. Write with words, draw with images, or scrapbook with found objects. This can serve as amnesia

therapy at any time to recall you back
to your calling in life.

Four Word Poem: _____

Four Word Poem: _____

Four Word Poem: _____

Four Word Poem: _____

Four Word Poem:_____

Four Word Poem: _____

Four Word Poem: _____

Four Word Poem: _____

Four Word Poem: _____

Four Word Poem: _____

Four Word Poem: _____

Four Word Poem: _____

Four Word Poem: _____

Four Word Poem: _____

Four Word Poem: _____

Four Word Poem: _____

Four Word Poem: _____

Four Word Poem: _____

Four Word Poem: _____

Four Word Poem: _____

Four Word Poem: _____

ABOUT THE AUTHOR

Marlon F. Hall is a lecturing anthropologist, practitioner, and storyteller who uses film, art-installations, salon dinner parties, and yoga to unearth beauty from brokenness.

He helps individuals and organizations develop sustainable practices, rituals, values, and programs that deepen their connections, strengthen their culture and broaden their impact.

Marlon serves as the Principal for his private anthropological based consulting practice, the Director for Folklore Films, and a Yoga Teacher at Big Power Yoga.

His life intention is to cultivate human potential in ways that are whimsically beautiful and positively willful.

WWW.MARLONHALL.COM

INFO@MARLONHALL.COM

@MARLONFHALL

Printed in Poland
by Amazon Fulfillment
Poland Sp. z o.o., Wrocław